D0258226

How to use this book

Follow the advice, in italics, given for teachers on each page.
Praise *the children at every step!*

Detailed guidance is provided in the Read Write Inc. Phonics Handbook

8 reading activities

Children:
- *Practise reading the speed sounds.*
- *Read the green and red words for the story.*
- *Listen as you read the introduction.*
- *Discuss the vocabulary check with you.*
- *Read the story.*
- *Re-read the story and discuss the 'questions to talk about'.*
- *Re-read the story with fluency and expression.*
- *Practise reading the speed words.*

Speed sounds

Consonants   *Say the pure sounds (do not add 'uh').*

f ff	l ll	m	n	r	s	v (ve)	z s	(sh)	(th)	(ng) nk

b bb	c k ck	d	g gg	h	j	p	qu	t	w wh	x	y	ch (tch)

Vowels   *Say the sounds in and out of order.*

at	hen	in	on	up	day	see	high	blow	zoo

*Each box contains one sound but sometimes more than one grapheme. Focus graphemes are **circled**.*

Green words

Read in Fred Talk (sounds).

rub wi<u>tch</u> went cat ha<u>ve</u> had

<u>fi</u><u>sh</u> pi<u>ng</u> di<u>sh</u> milk soft bed

Read the root word first and then with the ending.

wi<u>sh</u> → wi<u>sh</u>es

Red words

I <u>the</u> s<u>ai</u>d <u>you</u> of

Vocabulary check

Discuss the meaning (as used in the story) after the children have read each word.

definition:

lamp   *small light (rub this lamp)*

wishes   *things you really want (You can have 3 wishes)*

Punctuation to note in this story:

Stitch	*Capital letter for witch's name*
Rub Ping Rub	*Capital letters that start sentences*
.	*Full stop at the end of each sentence*
!	*Exclamation mark used to show anger and surprise*
…	*Wait and see*

Stitch the witch

Introduction

If you could have three wishes what would they be?
Stitch the witch must be in a good mood today because she
has decided to give her cat three wishes. Stitch can't even
get this right!

What do you think might go wrong?

Story written by Gill Munton
Illustrated by Tim Archbold

"Rub this lamp,"
said Stitch the witch,
"then you can have
3 wishes."

Rub-a-dub-dub, went the cat.
"I wish I had ... a fish."

Ping!

Ping!

Rub-a-dub-dub, went the cat.

"I wish I had ...
a dish of milk."

Ping!

Rub-a-dub-dub, went the cat.

"I wish I had ...
a soft bed."

Ping!

Questions to talk about

FIND IT QUESTIONS

✓ *Turn to the page*

✓ *Read the question to the children*

✓ *Find the answer*

Page 8:   *Why does the cat rub the lamp?*
What does he say to make the magic work?
What is his first wish?

Page 10:   *What is his second wish?*

Page 12:   *What is his third wish?*

Page 13:   *What does Stitch think about what has happened?*
(Look at the picture to help: angry / cross / furious / frustrated)